A Pocket Guide to the
Ladybirds
of Britain and Ireland

by
Bryan J Pinchen

Published by
Forficula Books, 7 Brookland Close, Pennington, Lymington,
Hampshire, SO41 8JE

First published 2005

Printed by
The Romsey Group, Mayflower Close, Chandlers Ford Industrial
Estate, Chandlers Ford, Eastleigh, Hampshire. SO53 4AR

© Copyright 2005

All text and illustrations copyright Bryan J Pinchen 2005

All rights reserved. No part of this publication may be reproduced,
stored in a retrieval system, or transmitted in any form by
any means, electronic, mechanical, photo-copying, recording, or
otherwise, without the prior permission of the copyright owner.

ISBN 0-9549349-1-1

A Pocket Guide to the Ladybirds of Britain and Ireland.

cover: 7-spot Ladybird *Coccinella 7-punctata*

Contents

Introduction

Ladybirds are amongst our most familiar and best known insects. Few people realize that in Britain the ladybird family contains over 40 species. A number of these are small, rarely encountered and difficult to identify without the aid of a microscope. Twenty-seven species of the family are easily recognisable as ladybirds, possessing bright colours and a variable number and colour of spots or streaks. Two of these, the 12-spot and 13-spot Ladybirds are considered extinct and are not included here. Two species which have recently started to colonise Britain, the Bryony Ladybird and the Harlequin Ladybird, are included. This book deals with the 25 species which can easily be recognised as ladybirds.

All the ladybirds covered by this book can be identified by looking at their overall colour and counting the number, colour and position of any spots or streaks. Other useful identification features, such as markings on the *pronotum*, underside of the body, and the colour of the legs, are included here to help confirm your identification.

Some species show a great variation in the number of spots or streaks and general colour. Where variations within a species occur these are noted in the text and, in some instances, a few of the most common variations are illustrated.

This book is divided into four parts:
- recognising ladybirds
- the life cycle and habits of ladybirds
- identification
- recording ladybirds and suggested further reading

Both 'common' and scientific names are used throughout the text and follow those on the most recently published checklist. Common names are in wide use, have changed little over the years and largely relate to the number of spots present in typical specimens. For practical purposes the numbers in the scientific name are often shown as figures, e.g. *Coccinella septempunctata* becomes *Coccinella 7-punctata*.

All specimens have been painted from my own reference collection and specimens housed in the collection of Hampshire County Council Museums and Archives Service, Winchester.

I would like thank the many friends who not only prompted this work, but who also assisted with the content and layout. In particular I would like to thank Bob Lord, Chris Palmer, Linda Smith, Christine Taylor and Alex Williams.

Recognising Ladybirds

Ladybirds, like most adult beetles, are characterised by their hardened forewings that meet in the centre to form a protective cover for the hind wings. The hardened forewings are known as *elytra*. Where the elytra join there is a hardened triangular area known as the *scutellum*. The hindwings are flexible and folded beneath the elytra when not needed for flight. Behind the head, the thorax is covered by a protective shield known as the pronotum. When viewed from above ladybirds are largely rounded or oval, when viewed from the side they appear dome-shaped.

Another family of beetles, the Leaf Beetles (Chrysomelidae), are similar in size, shape and appearance and occur in the same habitats as ladybirds. However, many leaf beetles are metallic coloured and lack the combination of brightly coloured elytra with spots or streaks. Many species are parallel-sided when viewed from above.

Other major differences between these two groups are:
Ladybirds: Antennae short and club-tipped. Feet appearing to have three segments when viewed with a low magnification lens.
Leaf beetles: Antennae long and almost filamentous. Feet appearing to have four segments when viewed with a low magnification lens.

Ladybirds

Antennae short
and clubbed

Feet appearing to
have 3 segments

Leaf Beetles

Antennae long
and filamentous

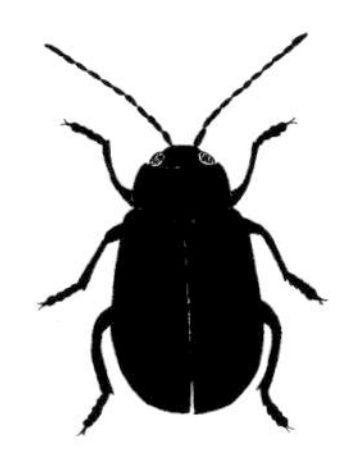

Feet appearing to
have 4 segments

Features mentioned in the text

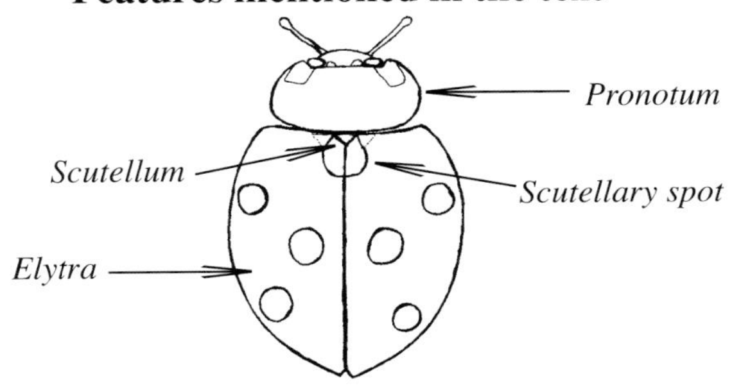

Life Cycle

For the purposes of this book, we will begin the ladybird life cycle on a warm day in early spring. Adults emerge from their hibernation sites and disperse to surrounding scrub, woodland, heaths, grassland, gardens and even reedbeds. Some species which have hibernated high in the tree canopy will remain there.

Following mating the females lay their eggs on leaves, plant stems, the developing buds of conifer needles, or amongst leaf litter and debris. In warm conditions the eggs hatch after a few days, and the newly hatched larvae seek out food. Aphids form the staple diet for many ladybirds, with some feeding on only a single species of aphid. Other ladybirds feed on scale and sap-sucking insects. Two species feed exclusively on vegetation, and three species feed on moulds and mildews.

Many ladybird larvae are blackish-grey in colour with a variable amount of yellowish or orange streaking and spots. In many ways they resemble bird droppings; a possible deterrent to predators.

a ladybird larva

The larvae may take between two and four weeks to reach maturity, during which time they will moult three times as they grow larger. When they have reached maturity they pupate, emerging as adults just a few weeks later. Typically only one generation is produced each year.

All our species overwinter as adults and seek out places to hibernate towards the end of the summer. Hibernation sites are in locations where the temperature will remain constant and, if possible, frost-free for prolonged periods. Some species hibernate amongst leaf litter and debris, some around the bases of trees and shrubs or around buildings and window frames, some beneath bark, and others in developing buds of conifer needles. On some occasions many hundreds or even thousands of individuals of the same (or different) species may cluster together around the bases of trees and shrubs.

The bright colours of the adult ladybirds serve to warn predators, such as birds, small mammals and other predatory insects, of their unpleasant taste. This is further backed up by the adults producing a foul-smelling liquid from between the leg joints when they are attacked or handled roughly. The bright colours and patterns can also provide camouflage; this is particularly apparent in the Striped Ladybird which can be hard to find when hidden amongst developing pine needles.

Identification

Most ladybirds can be identified by noting the colour of the elytra and counting the number and colour of spots or streaks present. In some species the markings on the pronotum need to be examined too. The underside colour and any markings are also useful features to note, along with leg colour. Many species retract their legs when handled or turned on their backs allowing easy observation of the underside.

Some species are very variable in their number and positioning of spots and these variations can cause identification problems. Adults newly emerged from pupae lack bright colouration and may also cause identification problems.

If you cannot recognise your ladybird specimen from these pictures consult one of the identification guides listed on page 61.

In the following pages the most commonly found ladybird colouration is the main illustration. Where there are variations, some of the most commonly found are illustrated.
The 2-spot, 10-spot and Harlequin Ladybirds show the most variation of all the species and space permits only a few variations to be illustrated here.

To make identification easier, here are a few questions to ask yourself once you have found a ladybird.

- What colour are the elytra?
- What colour are the spots or streaks?
- How many spots or streaks are there?
- What colour is the underside?
- What colour are the legs?
- Are there any markings on the pronotum?

After determining the above, turn to the identification pictures and compare your specimen. In most cases it should be possible to make an accurate identification.

In the following pages, the 'red' and 'orange' species are shown as those with black spots first, followed by species with white or pale spots.

The three 'black' species all possess a 'rim' around the edge of their elytra. Some varieties of the 2-spot, 10-spot and Harlequin Ladybirds may be black with red spots, but lack this rim - a useful identification feature in case of difficulty.

Upperside: Typically red with seven black spots, the scutellum is bordered by small white triangles.

Pronotum: Black with white squares on the front edge.

Underside: Black with a single white triangle between the front and middle pairs of legs.

Legs: Black.

Length: 7 mm.

Habitat: Most habitats including gardens, woodland, grassland, heathland, coast and moorland.

Food: Aphids.

Similar species: The Scarce 7-spot Ladybird and a variation of the 5-spot Ladybird may be confused with this species but habitat and the underside markings should help confirm your identification.

Variations: Typically with only seven spots, these can vary in size and strength of colouration, sometimes with no spots, five spots or up to nine spots. A very rare all black form occurs.

7-spot Ladybird
Coccinella 7-punctata

One of the most common ladybird species, found throughout England, Wales, Scotland and Ireland.

Underside

Upperside: Typically red with two black spots.

Pronotum: Black with broad white edges leading from front to back, a small white spot at the back of the pronotum varies in size and shape.

Underside: Black.

Legs: Black.

Length: 4 mm.

Habitat: Most habitats including gardens, woodland, grassland, heathland, coast and moorland.

Food: Aphids.

Similar species: Some of the varieties of this species can be confused with the 5-spot, 7-spot, 10-spot, 11-spot, Pine, Kidney-spot and Harlequin Ladybirds.

Variations: Over 100 different varieties have been recorded, usually the differences are confined to the colour and number of spots on the elytra. The legs are always black despite the elytra variation. There is no 'rim' around the edge of the elytra or keel at the tip providing a useful means of separating this species from the Pine, Kidney-spot and Harlequin Ladybirds.

2-spot Ladybird
Adalia 2-punctata

One of the most common ladybird species, found throughout England, Wales and Scotland with scattered records from Ireland.

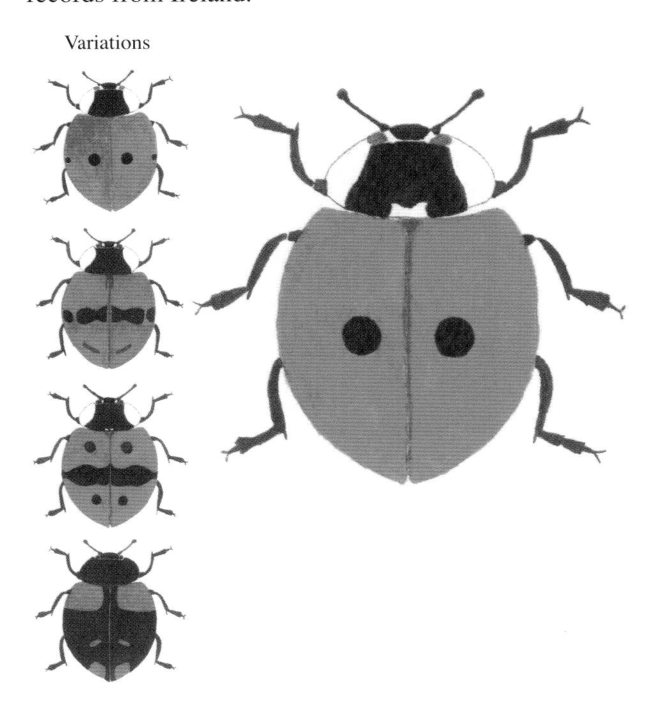

Upperside: Typically red with ten black spots.

Pronotum: White or off-white with distinctive, but variable, black wedge-shaped markings.

Underside: Black.

Legs: Pale brown.

Length: 4 mm.

Habitat: Most habitats including gardens, woodland, grassland, heathland, coast and moorland.

Food: Aphids.

Similar species: Some of the varieties may be confused with the 2-spot, Cream-streaked, Harlequin, Pine and Kidney-spot Ladybirds.

Variations: A huge number of variations occur, the colour forms illustrated appear most frequently. The legs are always pale brown; a useful identification feature. There is no 'rim' around the edge of the elytra or keel at the tip providing a useful means of separating this species from the Pine, Kidney-spot and Harlequin Ladybirds.

10-spot Ladybird

Adalia 10-punctata

One of the most common ladybird species, found throughout England, Wales and Scotland with scattered records from Ireland.

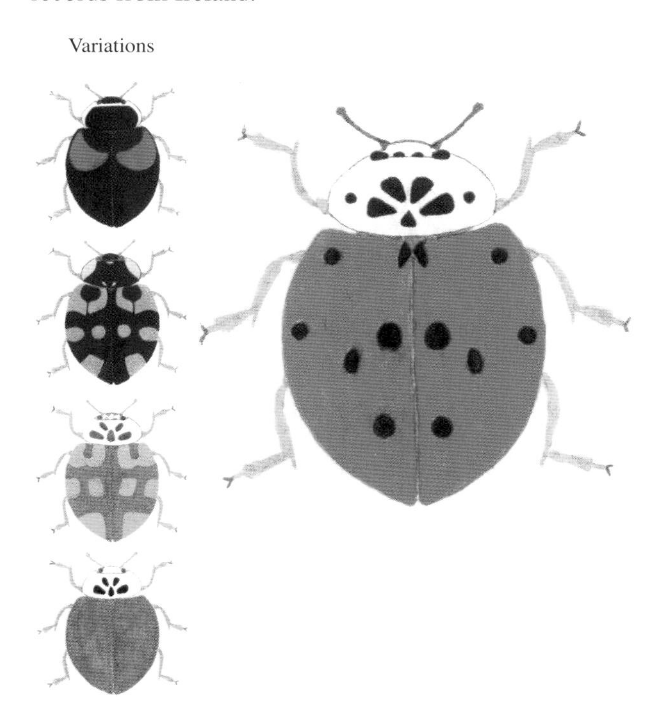

Upperside: Typically red with eleven black spots, the scutellum is white and bordered by small white triangles. The scutellary spot is black.

Pronotum: Black with white squares on the front edge and a thin white side border.

Underside: Black.

Legs: Black.

Length: 5 mm.

Habitat: Largely found in damp grasslands near the coast, however it does occur inland on both dry and moist grassland sites.

Food: Aphids.

Similar species: The 7-spot Ladybird may cause confusion with the seven-spotted form of this species, but the white scutellum, all black underside and brown antennae of this species should confirm your identification.

Variations: Typically with eleven spots, but forms with seven or nine spots occur frequently.

11-spot Ladybird

Coccinella 11-punctata

A common ladybird species, found throughout England, Wales and Scotland with scattered records from Ireland.

Upperside: Typically red with eighteen black spots of variable size. Each of the black spots is usually surrounded by a pale cream ring.

Pronotum: Black with a broad white, wavy-edged border and two white spots on the back edge.

Underside: Black with a single white triangle between the front and middle pairs of legs. The underside may sometimes be a dark orange-brown.

Legs: Black.

Length: 9 mm.

Habitat: Conifer woodland, with a preference for areas with mature Scots Pine.

Food: Aphids.

Similar species: None.

Variations: Typically with eighteen spots, but specimens without any spots or with up to twenty-two spots occur. Occasionally the pale rings are missing, or the black spots are missing, but the distinctive pronotum markings remain constant. A rare all black form occurs.

Eyed Ladybird
Anatis ocellata

A common and widespread ladybird species, found in scattered populations across much of England, Wales, Scotland and Ireland.

Underside

Upperside: Typically dark red with sixteen black spots, often with variable orange streaking. The scutellum is bordered with small creamy-white triangles.

Pronotum: White with a distinctive pattern of eleven black spots and wedges.

Underside: Variable, dark brown or reddish-brown, but with extensive white areas between the front and middle pairs of legs, and extensively pale beneath the head.

Legs: Reddish-brown.

Length: 7 mm.

Habitat: Conifer woodland and plantations, with a preference for areas with mature Scots Pine.

Food: Aphids.

Similar species: The markings on the pronotum may cause confusion with the 10-spot Ladybird, but the underside markings should help confirm your identification.

Variations: Typically with sixteen black spots, but frequently with only four on the edges of the elytra. The extent of orange streaking on the elytra varies considerably. A rare all black form occurs.

Cream-streaked Ladybird

Harmonia 4-punctata

A scarce ladybird species, found in scattered locations in southern and eastern England, with some records from the north. Not recorded from Ireland.

Variations

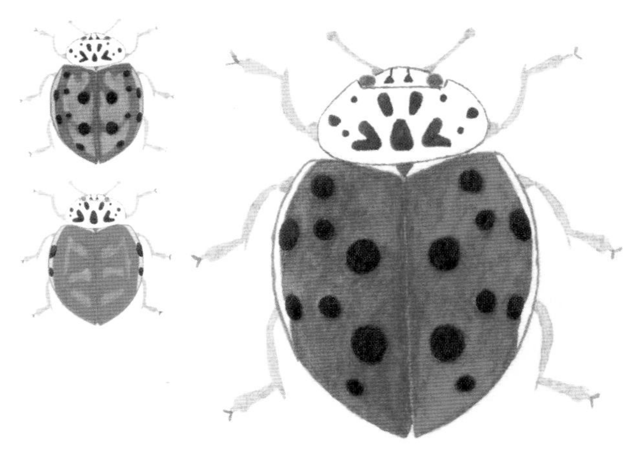

Underside

Upperside: Typically deep reddish, with twenty-four black spots on the elytra. There is a covering of fine, dense, and almost transparent hairs on the elytra.

Pronotum: The same colour as the elytra, also covered with fine hairs, there may often be a central dark spot.

Underside: Black.

Legs: Reddish-brown, similar in colour to the elytra.

Length: 4 mm.

Habitat: Wet and dry grassland, meadows and scrub edge habitats.

Food: Vegetarian, feeding on the leaves of a wide range of herbaceous plants.

Similar species: None.

Variations: The most commonly found variation has only twenty spots. Other variations may vary from having no spots at all to having as many as twenty-six. A rare all black form occurs. The presence of fine hairs on the elytra should help to confirm your identification.

24-spot Ladybird

Subcoccinella 24-punctata

A common and widespread ladybird species, found across much of central and southern England and Wales, but rarer in Scotland.

Upperside: Typically red with six black spots towards the rear of the elytra, often with much smaller black spots at the front edge of the elytra. The black scutellum is bordered by small white triangles.

Pronotum: Black with white front and edges and a white spot on each side of the centre line.

Underside: Black with a white triangle between the front and middle pairs of legs and the middle and hind pairs of legs.

Legs: Black.

Length: 6 mm.

Habitat: Found in a range of habitats including grasslands, woodland edge and scrub, usually associated with sandy soils.

Food: Aphids.

Similar species: The 7-spot and Scarce 7-spot Ladybirds may cause some confusion with this species but the pronotum markings should help confirm your identification.

Variations: Typically with only seven spots but variations with up to fifteen spots are frequent.

Adonis' Ladybird
Adonia variegata

A widespread but scarce ladybird species, largely confined to central and southern England.

Underside

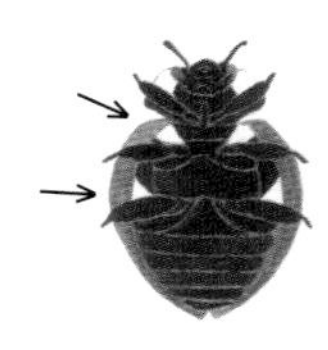

Upperside: Typically reddish-pink or brownish-pink, but also an overall sandy brown colour, typically with nineteen black spots.

Pronotum: The same colour as the elytra, with six distinctive black wedges.

Underside: Black with a single white triangle between the front two pairs of legs.

Legs: Reddish-pink or brownish-pink.

Length: 4 mm.

Habitat: Damp grassland, coastal marshes and reedbeds.

Food: Aphids.

Similar species: None.

Variations: Typically with nineteen spots, but variations with as few as fifteen spots or as many as twenty-one spots occur frequently. The elongate shape of this species should help confirm your identification.

Water Ladybird
Anisosticta 19-punctata

A common and widespread ladybird species, found across much of central and southern England, parts of Wales and the extreme south west of Ireland.

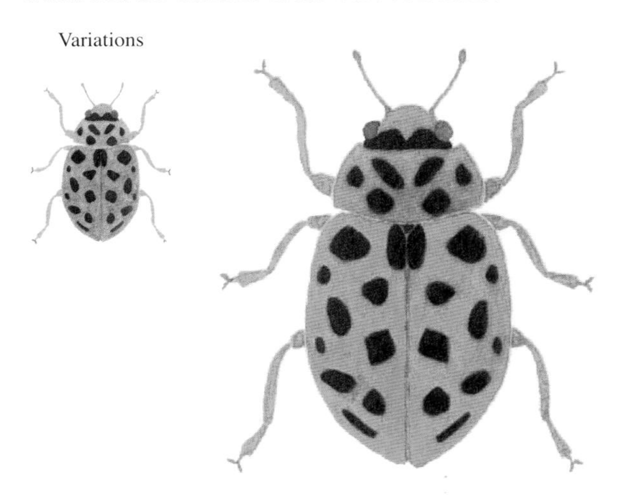

Upperside: Typically red with two black streaks running down the elytra and two large black spots towards the rear. The scutellary spot extends down the elytra.

Pronotum: Black with white rectangles on the front edge.

Underside: Black.

Legs: Black.

Length: 4 mm.

Habitat: Dry sandy heathland.

Food: Aphids.

Similar species: None.

Variations: The two dark streaks running down the elytra may be broken to appear more like spots or a pair of 'commas' on the front edge. A combination of six dark markings are typical, but varieties without marks do occur. An all black form also occurs.

Hieroglyphic Ladybird
Coccinella hieroglyphica

A scarce but widespread ladybird species, found on heathlands throughout England, Wales, Scotland and Ireland.

Variations

Upperside: Typically red with seven or nine black spots. The spots at the front edge of the elytra are often small or absent. The scutellum is bordered by small white triangles.

Pronotum: Black with white squares on the front edge.

Underside: Black with a white triangle between the front and middle pairs of legs and the middle and hind pairs of legs.

Legs: Black.

Length: 7 mm.

Habitat: Dry sandy heathlands in southern England.

Food: Possibly wood ants or their larvae/pupae or perhaps aphids found within wood ant nests.

Similar species: The 7-spot and 5-spot Ladybirds may cause some confusion, but the underside markings and habitat should help to separate these species.

Variations: Typically with seven or nine spots, the front two spots being reduced, but forms with less than this or as many as eleven spots occur.

Scarce 7-spot Ladybird
Coccinella magnifica

A rare ladybird species, seemingly confined to southern heathlands in Hampshire, Dorset and Surrey.

Underside

Upperside: Typically red with five black spots, the scutellum is bordered by small white triangles.

Pronotum: Black with white squares on the front edge.

Underside: Black with a single white triangle between the front and middle pairs of legs.

Legs: Black.

Length: 5 mm.

Habitat: Amongst river gravels and unstable river shingles.

Food: Presumed to be aphids.

Similar species: The 7-spot and Scarce 7-spot Ladybirds may cause some confusion.

Variations: Typically with only five spots, but sometimes as many as seven occur, causing some confusion with the 7-spot and Scarce 7-spot Ladybirds. Habitat, underside markings and the brown antennae of this species should help confirm your identification.

5-spot Ladybird
Coccinella 5-punctata

An extremely rare ladybird species, confined to a few sites in Wales and Scotland. There are old records in southern England from Devon and Dorset.

Underside

Upperside: Typically a deep reddish-brown with fourteen pale cream spots.

Pronotum: The same colour as the elytra with small cream coloured 'commas' on back edge.

Underside: Deep reddish-brown.

Legs: Reddish-brown.

Length: 5 mm.

Habitat: Hedgerows, scrub and deciduous woodland.

Food: Aphids.

Similar species: Confusion may occur with the 18-spot Ladybird, but the underside markings should separate these two species.

Variations: Almost always deep reddish with fourteen pale cream spots, this species appears not to show any variation at all. A very rare all black form may sometimes occur.

Cream-spot Ladybird

Calvia 14-guttata

A common and widespread ladybird species, found across much of England, Wales and Scotland, with scattered populations in eastern and Northern Ireland.

Upperside: Typically deep reddish-coloured with eighteen pale cream spots. The scutellum is bordered by a distinctive cream coloured star marking.

Pronotum: The same colour as the elytra, with a broad pale cream border and a single pale patch at the front and two pale patches at the back.

Underside: Reddish-coloured like the elytra, with a white bar running down between the legs and dark smudges on the centre of the abdominal segments.

Legs: Deep reddish.

Length: 4 mm.

Habitat: Conifer woodland with a preference for areas with mature Scots Pine.

Food: Aphids.

Similar species: Confusion may occur with the Cream-spot Ladybird, but the underside markings should separate these two species.

Variations: Typically has eighteen spots, but may occasionally have only fourteen or sixteen spots.

18-spot Ladybird
Myrrha 18-guttata

A locally common and widespread ladybird species, found scattered across much of England and Wales. Rarer in Scotland and Ireland.

Underside

Upperside: Highly variable but often reddish-orange with up to nineteen black spots. There is a distinctive keel running around the rear edge of the elytra.

Pronotum: Typically white with a thick black 'M'-shaped mark.

Underside: Orange-brown with dark areas centrally and on the abdominal segments. Extensively pale beneath the head and pronotum.

Legs: Reddish or yellowish-brown.

Length: 8 mm.

Habitat: Most habitats including gardens, woodland, and grassland.

Food: Aphids, but also lacewings, scale insects, caterpillars and even other ladybird larvae.

Similar species: Some of the varieties may be confused with the 2-spot, 10-spot, Cream-streaked, Pine and Kidney-spot Ladybirds.

Variations: A huge number of varieties occur but the large size, keel on the rear of the elytra and the underside markings should help confirm your identification.

Harlequin Ladybird
Harmonia axyridis

A recent colonist which has been spreading north and westwards from southern and eastern England since 2004.

Variations

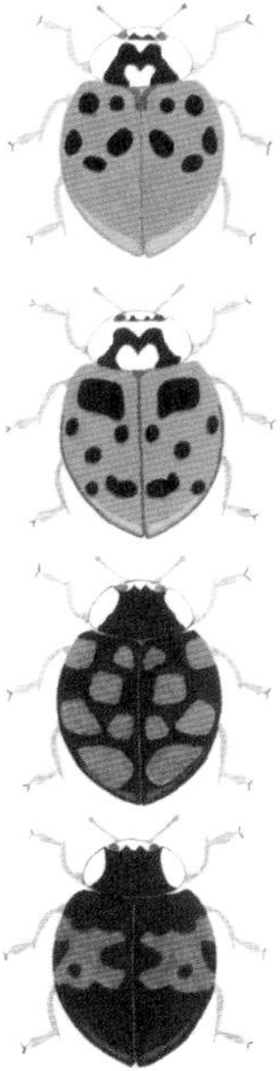

Underside

Upperside: Typically reddish-orange with eleven black spots. There is a fine covering of pale hairs on the elytra.

Pronotum: The same colour as the elytra.

Underside: Reddish-orange.

Legs: Reddish-orange.

Length: 7 mm

Habitat: Most habitats where the food plant grows, including grassland, scrub and woodland edge.

Food: Vegetarian, feeding almost exclusively on White Bryony. Other members of the Bryony family will also be eaten.

Similar species: None.

Variations: None recorded.

Bryony Ladybird
Henosepilachna argus

A recent colonist in southern and eastern England which appears to be slowly spreading north and westwards.

Upperside: Typically bright orange with sixteen cream-coloured spots. There is an almost transparent 'rim' around the edge of the elytra.

Pronotum: The same colour as the elytra with broad white edges at the front and back corners.

Underside: Orange-brown with a white bar between the middle and hind pairs of legs.

Legs: Orange brown.

Length: 7 mm.

Habitat: Deciduous or coniferous woodland, scrub and hedgerows, often with a preference for areas with Sycamore. This species frequently flies at night to illuminated windows and moth traps.

Food: Feeds almost exclusively on mildew on the leaves of deciduous trees. Will also eat honeydew and sometimes small aphids.

Similar species: None.

Variations: Typically with only sixteen spots, but occasionally may have fourteen or eighteen spots.

Orange Ladybird
Halyzia 16-guttata

A local ladybird species, found in scattered populations in central and southern England and Wales. Rarer in Scotland and Northern Ireland.

Upperside: Typically orange brown with thirteen pale cream-coloured streaks and spots, The scutellum is cream-coloured and bordered by small cream triangles.

Pronotum: Largely white or cream with an orange-brown central band often bordered by darker bands.

Underside: Orange-brown, with a white triangle between the middle and hind pairs of legs.

Length: 8 mm.

Habitat: Conifer woodland, with a preference for areas with mature Scots Pine.

Food: Aphids.

Similar species: None.

Variations: Typically the markings form thirteen spots and streaks, but this can vary from none at all to fifteen spots and streaks. A rare all black form occurs.

Striped Ladybird
Myzia oblongoguttata

A scarce but widespread ladybird species, found in scattered populations across England, Wales, Scotland and Ireland.

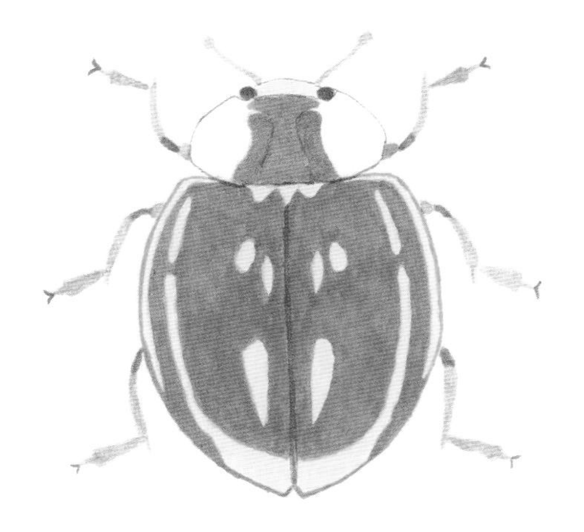

Upperside: Typically orange-brown to yellowish-brown or tan coloured. Usually lacking darker or lighter spots or streaks.

Pronotum: White to cream-coloured with a distinctive dark brown 'M'-shaped mark towards the back edge.

Underside: Variable, often dark beneath the head and between the legs with white side patches and an orange-brown abdomen.

Legs: Orange-brown.

Length: 5 mm.

Habitat: Most closely associated with conifer woodland and plantations.

Food: Sap-sucking insects closely related to aphids, but will also feed on aphids.

Similar species: Confusion may occur with unspotted forms of the Harlequin Ladybird. The small size and lack of a keel on the rear edge of the elytra should help confirm your identification.

Variations: Typically with no spots on the elytra, but may have four or six streaks and spots. A rare all black or dark brown form occurs.

Larch Ladybird
Aphidecta obliterata

A common and widespread ladybird species, found across much of England, Wales, Scotland, eastern and Northern Ireland.

Variations

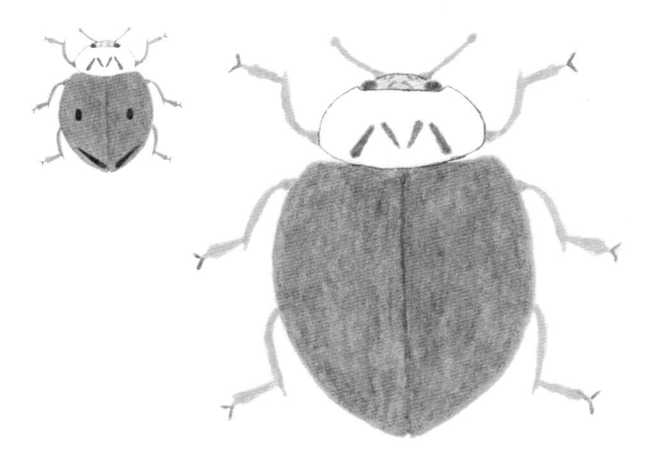

Upperside: Typically bright yellow with fourteen almost square black spots, some of which are often joined or almost touching. There is a slight 'rim' around the edge of the elytra.

Pronotum: Yellow with a broad four-pointed black mark on the back edge.

Underside: Black with white triangles between the front and middle pairs of legs and the middle and hind pairs of legs.

Legs: Pale brown ringed with black on the upper leg.

Length: 4 mm.

Habitat: Most habitats including gardens, woodland, grassland, heathland, coast and moorland.

Food: Aphids.

Similar species: None.

Variations: Typically has fourteen spots, although specimens may occur with any number of spots between four and fourteen. The black spots may be fused to give the appearance of a black ladybird with squarish yellow spots. A rare all black form occurs.

14-spot Ladybird
Propylea 14-punctata

A common and widespread ladybird species, found across much of England and Wales, but becoming rarer in Scotland and Ireland.

Upperside: Typically a dirty straw-yellow colour with sixteen black spots, these are often joined to form a distinctive wavy band on the sides.

Pronotum: The same colour as the elytra, with six distinctive black wedge-shaped marks.

Underside: Black with a pale spot between the middle and hind pairs of legs.

Legs: Largely pale brown.

Length: 3 mm.

Habitat: Occurs in wet and dry grassland, meadows and scrubby habitats.

Food: Feeds exclusively on powdery mildews.

Similar species: None.

Variations: Typically with only sixteen spots, some of these are fused to form a band along the edges. Specimens with eighteen spots also occur. A rare all black form occurs.

16-spot Ladybird

Tytthaspis 16-punctata

A common and widespread ladybird species in central and southern England, but records appear sparse for Wales and northern England. Not recorded in Scotland or Ireland.

Upperside: Typically bright yellow with twenty-two rounded black spots.

Pronotum: The same colour as the elytra with four distinctive black spots and a black triangle on the back edge.

Underside: Black with pale yellow triangles between the front and middle pairs of legs and the middle and hind pairs of legs.

Legs: Largely pale brown with a darker streak on the outer edges.

Length: 4 mm.

Habitat: In wet and dry grassland, meadows and scrub edge.

Food: Feeds exclusively on powdery mildews.

Similar species: None.

Variations: Typically with twenty-two spots, but occasionally specimens with only twenty spots are found. The distinctive pronotum markings should help confirm your identification.

22-spot Ladybird
Psyllobora 22-punctata

A common and widespread ladybird species, found across much of England and Wales, but becoming scarce in the north and Scotland. Widespread but scarce in eastern and Northern Ireland.

Upperside: Shiny black with four red spots that appear to form two red bars. The edge of the elytra is flattened to form a 'rim'.

Pronotum: Shiny black, the head is a deep reddish-brown colour.

Underside: Black, becoming ginger-brown towards the extreme tip of the abdomen.

Legs: Black.

Length: 4 mm.

Habitat: In dry or wet heathland, gorse scrub and conifer woodland.

Food: Scale insects but also aphids and sap-sucking insects.

Similar species: Confusion may occur with the Pine and Kidney-spot Ladybirds, but the reddish-coloured head and the underside colouration should help confirm your identification. Black-coloured 2-spot, 10-spot and Harlequin Ladybirds lack the 'rim' around the elytra.

Variations: Little variation occurs, but occasionally only two spots may be present.

Heather Ladybird
Chilocorus 2-pustulatus

A common and widespread ladybird species in southern and central England and Wales with isolated records from eastern Ireland. Not recorded from Scotland.

Underside

Upperside: Shiny black with two large red spots on the elytra. The edge of the elytra is flattened to form a 'rim'.

Pronotum: Shiny black, with a black head.

Underside: Black with extensive ginger-brown towards the tip of the abdomen.

Length: 5 mm.

Habitat: Deciduous woodland, hedgerows and scrub.

Food: Aphids.

Similar species: Confusion may occur with the Pine and Heather Ladybirds, but the underside colouration should help confirm your identification. Black-coloured 2-spot, 10-spot and Harlequin Ladybirds lack the 'rim' around the elytra.

Variations: Little variation occurs, this species is typically found with only two red spots.

Kidney-spot Ladybird
Chilocorus renipustulatus

A widespread ladybird species, found in central and southern England and Wales, with isolated records from Scotland. Not recorded from Ireland.

Underside

Upperside: Shiny black with two red 'comma' marks on the front of the elytra and two red spots towards the back of the elytra. The edge of the elytra is flattened to form a 'rim'.

Pronotum: Shiny black, with a black head.

Underside: Black, becoming orange-brown towards the tip of the abdomen, with an orange band running between both pairs of legs.

Legs: Black.

Length: 5 mm.

Habitat: Conifer woodland, heathland and often in gorse, occasionally found on deciduous trees.

Food: Scale insects but also aphids and sap-sucking insects.

Similar species: Confusion may occur with the Kidney-spot and Heather Ladybirds, but the underside colouration should help confirm your identification. Black-coloured 2-spot, 10-spot and Harlequin Ladybirds lack the 'rim' around the elytra.

Variations: Typically with four spots, but occasionally specimens with only two spots may be found.

Pine Ladybird

Exochomus 4-pustulatus

A common and widespread ladybird species, across most of southern and central England and Wales, with a few records from Scotland. Not recorded from Ireland.

Underside

Recording Ladybirds

Ladybirds can be found in most habitats and localities in Britain and Ireland. As you become more interested in this group there will be occasions when specimens cannot be identified in the field. To enable accurate identification reference or 'voucher' specimens may need to be collected. These can be humanely killed in an entomologists' killing jar (or left in the freezer for 24 hours), mounted and set - for details see page 61. It is important to remember that only single specimens should be taken from any one site. Voucher specimens can also be compared with material housed in certain local, national and university museum collections.

Recording ladybirds can help map their distribution and determine declines or increases. Records of the Bryony and Harlequin Ladybirds will help monitor their spread. Records of all ladybirds, including the date and location, can be submitted to the National Recording Scheme at:

UK Ladybird Survey Team,
Biological Records Centre,
CEH Monks Wood,
PE28 2LS

Further information can be found at:
www.ladybird-survey.org
www.harlequin-survey.org

Further Reading

Some ladybirds may be difficult to identify from these pictures alone and it may be necessary to collect voucher specimens for critical identification. The following books contain further information.

Majerus, M & Kearns, P. (1989). *Ladybirds.* Naturalists' Handbooks 10. The Richmond Publishing Co. Ltd., P.O.Box 963, Slough. SL2 3RS

(For critical identification, a good key to all members of the ladybird family, details of how and where to find ladybirds, techniques for rearing and studying them, and details of how to mount specimens for a reference collection)

Hawkins, R. D. (2000) *Ladybirds of Surrey.* Surrey Wildlife Trust, School Lane, Pirbright, Woking, Surrey, GU24 0JN

(For colour photographs, a key to all the species and information on life cycles, biology, and habitats)

Species Index

This index includes only the page number for the start of each species identification page.

Elytra colour is indicated to aid cross-referencing with the illustrations.